HOW TO READ THIS STORY TO YOUR CHILD

Choose a quiet time during the day.

Sit next to your child with the book between you.

at the cover   about
icture. Ask   this
about?

This Is the Way

Previously published in Great Britain by Scholastic Publications Limited.

Copyright © 1992 by Anne Dalton.
All rights reserved. Published by Scholastic Inc., 730 Broadway,
New York, NY 10003, by arrangement with
Scholastic Publications Limited.
SCHOLASTIC HARDCOVER is a registered trademark of Scholastic Inc.

Library of Congress Cataloging-in-Publication Data.

Dalton, Anne.
    This is the way / story and pictures by Anne Dalton.
        p. cm.
    Summary: Rhythmic text in the tradition of the familiar nursery rhyme
follows children through a busy day.
    ISBN 0-590-45892-2
    1. Nursery rhymes.   2. Children's poetry, English. [1. Nursery
rhymes.   2. English poetry.]   I. Title.
    PZ8.3.D177Th   1992
    398.8 — dc20   91-42306
                                                                                  CIP
                                                                                   AC

12 11 10 9 8 7 6 5 4 3 2   2 3 4 5 6 7/9
                    Printed in the U.S.A.   37
            First Scholastic printing, September 1992

                The pictures in this book
                are crayon illustrations.

This Is the Way

Story and pictures by
Anne Dalton

SCHOLASTIC
HARDCOVER

SCHOLASTIC INC. / New York

This is the way we climb out of bed
Climb out of bed
Climb out of bed
This is the way we climb out of bed
On a cold and frosty morning

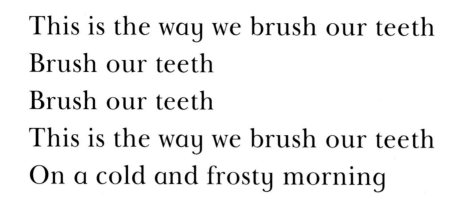

This is the way we brush our teeth
Brush our teeth
Brush our teeth
This is the way we brush our teeth
On a cold and frosty morning

This is the way we eat our breakfast
Eat our breakfast
Eat our breakfast
This is the way we eat our breakfast
On a cold and frosty morning

This is the way we skip to school
Skip to school
Skip to school
This is the way we skip to school
On a cold and frosty morning

This is the way we do our work
Do our work
Do our work
This is the way we do our work
In a warm and cozy classroom

This is the way we eat our lunch
Eat our lunch
Eat our lunch
This is the way we eat our lunch
At twelve o'clock in the lunchroom

This is the way we play our games
Play our games
Play our games
This is the way we play our games
In a cold and frosty playground

This is the way we paint our pictures
Paint our pictures
Paint our pictures
This is the way we paint our pictures
Back in the cozy classroom

This is the way we put on our coats
Put on our coats
Put on our coats
This is the way we put on our coats
And leave empty hooks in the classroom

This is the way we climb up and down
Climb up and down
Climb up and down
This is the way we climb up and down
While Dad stands holding the baby

This is the way we have our snack
Have our snack
Have our snack
This is the way we have our snack
On a cold and frosty evening

This is the way we go up the stairs
Go up the stairs
Go up the stairs
This is the way we go up the stairs
On a cold and frosty evening

This is the way we splash in the bath
Splash in the bath
Splash in the bath
This is the way we splash in the bath
On a cold and frosty evening

This is the way Dad reads us a story
Reads us a story
Reads us a story
This is the way Dad reads us a story
On a cold and frosty evening

This is the way Mom turns off the light
Turns off the light
Turns off the light
This is the way Mom turns off the light
On a cold and frosty evening

DATE DUE			